British Sporting Paintings

The production of this catalogue was made possible through the generosity of Mr. and Mrs. Paul Mellon. The research and editorial costs were partially funded by the Andrew W. Mellon Foundation.

The illustration for catalogue entry 51 on page 75 is reversed.

British Sporting Paintings

The Paul Mellon Collection
in the Virginia Museum of Fine Arts

by JUDY EGERTON

VIRGINIA MUSEUM OF FINE ARTS · RICHMOND
Distributed by the University of Washington Press, Seattle and London

Virginia Museum of Fine Arts, Richmond, Virginia 23221

Photographs by Joseph Szaszfai, Branford, Connecticut.

Printed in the United States of America.

LIBRARY OF CONGRESS CATALOGING-IN-PUBLICATION DATA
Virginia Museum of Fine Arts.
   British sporting paintings.

   Bibliography: p. 84.
   Includes index.
   1. Painting, British—Catalogs.   2. Painting, Modern—17th–18th centuries—
Great Britain—Catalogs.   3. Painting, Modern—19th century—Great Britain—
Catalogs.   4. Sports in art—Catalogs.   5. Painting—Virginia—Richmond—
Catalogs.   6. Mellon, Paul—Art collections—Catalogs.   7. Painting—Private
collections—Virginia—Richmond—Catalogs.   8. Virginia Museum of Fine
Arts—Catalogs. I. Egerton, Judy. II. Title.
ND1388.G7V57   1985   758'.3   85-22551
ISBN 0-917046-24-2
ISBN 0-917046-23-4 (pbk.)

COVER: John Wootton, *A Bay Horse Led Towards a Rubbing-Down House
at Newmarket* (catalogue number 1).

CONTENTS

FOREWORD

In 1938, just two years after the Virginia Museum of Fine Arts was inaugurated, Paul Mellon was elected to its Board of Trustees. He remained a faithful member of the board for the next forty years, a record of service, interest, and commitment unmatched in this or almost any other institution. His devotion to the ideals upon which the Museum was built has revealed itself not only in his personal service, but also in contributions that, for example, permitted the development of the first major addition to the Museum in 1954 and made possible the creation of the Virginia Museum Theatre—now Theatre Virginia—the Museum's longstanding partner in the pursuit of artistic excellence.

To Mr. Mellon's personal and financial support were added, from time to time, generous gifts or loans of objects from his own collection. In 1960 he helped organize and was a prominent lender to an exhibition that introduced equestrian art as a new subject to American audiences. The resulting exhibition, *Sport and the Horse*, drew not only from his own nascent collection of English sporting paintings, but also from internationally distinguished public and private collections. The equestrian subject was particularly appropriate, not only in view of Virginia's strong hunting tradition, but also because of the remarkable affinity in landscape between Virginia and England that is apparent in these paintings.

Another landmark exhibition was held here in 1963, when 451 paintings, drawings, watercolors, and illustrated books from the Mellon collection, presented as *Painting in England 1700–1850*, opened the doors on a singularly prolific era of British art that had too long gone unnoticed by American museums and collectors.

In 1968 Mr. Mellon gave to the Museum a major portion of a magnificent collection of Indian art that had been assembled by the late Nasli Heeramaneck and his wife, Alice. In so doing, he transformed the Indian art collection from one of modest proportion to one of international stature. And in 1983 he and Mrs. Mellon gave their superb collection of French paintings of the nineteenth and twentieth centuries, a gift particularly rich in Impressionist works.

Now, in addition to his generous contributions toward the construction of the West Wing and the opening of the Mellon Galleries, he presents a major collection of English eighteenth- and nineteenth-century paintings, drawings, and prints that will establish Richmond as a mecca for those concerned with the study of English landscape, and that conveys the intensity of man's involvement with the land, his enthusiasm for sport, his love of nature, and his understanding of domesticated animals. Few museums can testify to such continued generosity and confidence from a single patron.

This new collection, documented and analyzed in the following pages by the sympathetic and thoughtful expertise of Judy Egerton, Assistant Keeper, British Collection, at the Tate Gallery in London, introduces a particularly genteel world, one in which ceremony and refinement are, as it were, fused into a natural order of rolling hills, limpid skies, and vigorous vegetation. These picturesque landscapes and sporting scenes, closely observed and executed with love and understanding, have few parallels in western art.

The quality of these works and their serene elegance reflect the gentility and style of their donor. To him, and to Mrs. Mellon, who shares his collecting passion, the Commonwealth of Virginia is indeed grateful.

PAUL N. PERROT
Director

INTRODUCTION

ONE OF the Englishman's greatest joys is in field sports—they are all quite mad about them," observed François, future Duc de la Rochefoucauld, during a visit to England in 1784.[1] He also noted that the English "have an extraordinary affection for the horse—a passion which is common to the whole country."[2] Given this affection, it is not surprising that a general survey of the work of British sporting artists reveals a predominance of pictures of horse-racing and fox-hunting. That predominance is accurately reflected in this collection, although it includes pictures of shooting and fishing, and shows, in a charming picture by Pieter Angellis (catalogue no. 4), that the British will happily engage in a game of skittles, if no other diversion offers itself.

The sporting paintings, drawings, watercolours, and prints in Paul Mellon's magnificent gift to the Virginia Museum of Fine Arts reflect both the variety and the general quality of a uniquely British school of art during its heyday, the period from 1700 to 1850. In that period, a steadily increasing number of British artists concentrated their attention on producing pictures of sport and portraits of animals: the term "sporting art" hardly does justice to the variety of their subject-matter, which included portraits of exotic animals, coach-horses and prize cattle. Few of them produced masterpieces—George Stubbs is the only true genius in this field—but almost all of them produced vigorous images which appealed to most of their contemporaries, though not to those connoisseurs of art who considered that artists should attempt loftier themes than fox-hunting, horse-racing, and the breeding of thoroughbred horses and pedigree livestock.

In no other country did such a tradition of prolific and popular sporting art develop. Flemish painters such as Hondius and Snyders seemed to have eyes only for the savagery in scenes of boar-hunts, stag-hunts, and (in the case of Rubens) lion-hunts. French painters such as Desportes and Oudry concentrated chiefly on the ceremonial of the chase as pursued by the Court and the nobility. In Italy almost the only paintings which reflected a love of sport were some of Pompeo Batoni's portraits of English milords on the Grand Tour, who evidently felt more at ease if they were posed as they might have been if they were still at home in England, holding a sporting gun or accompanied by a favourite spaniel or whippet.

British sporting art derives its distinctive character from that

[1] François de la Rochefoucauld, *A Frenchman in England*, ed. Jean Marchand, trans. S. C. Roberts (1784; Cambridge, England: The University Press, 1933), p. 52.

[2] La Rochefoucauld, *Frenchman in England*, p. 74.

ix

other British speciality, the open-air portrait. Both reflect a taste for informality, an idealisation of leisure, and a love of country life. De la Rochefoucauld observed that the English country gentlemen "seem not to know what *ennui* is."[3] Contentment with country life radiates from paintings such as Ben Marshall's *Henry Legard with His Favourite Hunters* (catalogue no. 27), or John Frederick Herring's open-air portrait of Thomas Dawson, a much respected trainer of racehorses, at home in Yorkshire with his wife, children, family pony, and dog (catalogue no. 56). Dogs abound in British sporting art, whether they have been trained to work in the field, as George Stubbs's *Black and White Spaniel Following a Scent* evidently has (catalogue no. 8), or coaxed into more frivolous activities as in Philip Reinagle's *Portrait of an Extraordinary Musical Dog* (catalogue no. 11).

As many a picture of a hunter waiting patiently with a groom for his master shows, pictures do not have to portray strenuous activity to come within the category of sporting art. What sporting pictures must reflect, if they are to appeal to the British public, is cheerfulness, or that readiness for enjoyment with which Addison's character Sir Roger de Coverley set out for coursing in 1711: "The Brightness of the Weather, the Cheerfulness of every thing around me, the Chiding of the Hounds . . . the Hollowing of the Sportsmen, and the Sounding of the Horn, lifted my spirits into a most lively Pleasure."[4] It is just in that spirit of pleasurable anticipation that Peter Delmé and his friends are depicted riding over the Hampshire Downs in James Seymour's painting of 1738 (catalogue no. 5); in one of the best of all his paintings, Seymour manages to convey the feeling of a brisk early morning as the hunt

sets off over a seemingly endless landscape, over which the sun has not yet fully risen. Sporting pictures can communicate this sort of "lively Pleasure" even to armchair sportsmen; the reflection of a readiness for enjoyment perhaps explains why sporting prints so often hang in hotel dining rooms as images of conviviality.

Sometimes "cheerfulness" consists of putting the best possible face on mishaps and discomforts. Sports, as Robert Burton pointed out in his *Anatomy of Melancholy*, 1621, can be powerful antidotes to low spirits; and he noticed that many gentlemen who go angling "will wade up to the armholes upon such occasions, and voluntarily undertake that to satisfy their pleasure, which a poor man for a good stipend could scarce be hired to undergo."[5] The charms of the countryside and the freshness of the air offer abundant compensation for an empty bag or a fox "gone to earth." An unselfconscious celebration of the beauty of the landscape is evident throughout the best of British sporting art.

Demand for sporting and animal paintings increased in Britain from about 1700 as sporting life became better organised and more broadly based. There had been horse-races in Britain since the time of the Romans, but most race-meetings before 1700 were small local affairs. The systematic organisation of racing began in the early eighteenth century with the publication by 1728 of an annual calendar of racing events and the foundation by 1750 of the all-important Jockey Club to control and regulate racing. The most common racing event in the early eighteenth century had been the "match," in which one gentleman matched his horse against another's, usually for large stakes—as Mr. Lamego matched his chestnut horse, Driver, against Mr. Rogers's bay, Aaron, in Richard Roper's painting (catalogue no. 9). Between

[3] La Rochefoucauld, *Frenchman in England*, p. 48.

[4] Quoted by Sir Oliver Millar in his introduction to *British Sporting Paintings 1650–1850* (London: Arts Council, 1974–75), p. 10.

[5] Robert Burton, *Anatomy of Melancholy*, ed. Holbrook Jackson, vol. 2 (1968), p. 73.

1776 and 1814 the five Classic races—the St. Leger, the Oaks, the Derby, the Two Thousand Guineas, and the One Thousand Guineas—were established.

Newmarket, where some of the richest and most influential men of the day established the Jockey Club, drew increasingly large crowds. It also provided many sporting artists with their first important commissions. It provided John Wootton, the earliest artist represented here, with many of his early subjects. In Wootton's picture of *A Nobleman Arriving to Inspect Racehorses at Newmarket* (catalogue no. 3), the visitor is probably Lord Portmore but might have been any one of fifty noblemen of the day who were devoted to racing, breeding, and betting on racehorses. Horace Walpole complained in 1753 that "Nobody troubles their head . . . about anything but Newmarket, where the Duke of Cumberland is at present making a campaign, with half the nobility and half the money of England behind him; they really say, that not less than a hundred thousand pounds have been carried thither for the hazard of this single week."[6]

Racing scenes, not only at Newmarket but also at York, Doncaster, Ascot, Epsom, and many other towns, became increasingly colourful and increasingly crowded as racing colours were established and grandstands were built for spectators. Since the importation into England of the first Arabian stallions during the seventeenth century, immense care and considerable expense had gone into the breeding and training of the thoroughbred horse for the races. By 1784, de la Rochefoucauld could say that "from time immemorial" the British have "taken the greatest pride in the breeding of their horses; they treasure their pedigrees more jealously than their own."[7]

Paintings of celebrated stallions and pictures of brood mares and foals became almost as popular as racing scenes. James Ward's portrait of the brood mare Granadillo and her foal by Skyscraper is a fine example of this sort of subject (catalogue no. 28). The setting is rural, far from the noise and activity of the racetrack yet never wholly unconnected with it, for every owner and breeder must hope that a long-legged foal will in time prove a winner on the turf. Ben Marshall was to find "many a man who will give me fifty guineas for painting his horse, who thinks ten guineas too much for painting his wife."[8]

Fox-hunting, like racing, encouraged the breeding of the thoroughbred horse, and by the end of the eighteenth century the demand for fox-hunting pictures was just as great as for racing scenes. Once the deer and the hare had been the prime quarry for the hunt, but the shortage of deer by the end of the seventeenth century turned the attention of the English nobleman and squire to the fox. Fox-hunting encouraged the breeding of hounds with the nose, stamina, and speed to catch the fox. There is a wealth of difference, and a whole century of selective breeding, between the rather mixed and spindly hounds in James Ross's *A Meet of Foxhounds* of 1732 (catalogue no. 6) and the strong, deep-chested foxhounds in the foreground of John Frederick Herring's *A Hunting Morn* of circa 1840 (catalogue no. 54). Fox-hunting had once been effectively reserved for rich landowners who kept private packs of hounds at their own expense for their own diversion and that of their friends. From 1700, fox-hunting was increasingly financed by subscription, open to all, and by 1850 a hunt might have two or three hundred members. Robert Smith Surtees' hero John Jorrocks, a would-be hunting enthusiast, was "a great city grocer of the old school" who ended up as Master of the Handley Cross Foxhounds. Henry Alken, who illustrated *John Jorrocks's*

---

[6] Wilmarth S. Lewis, et al., eds., *Horace Walpole's Correspondence*, vol. 20 (1960), p. 373.
[7] La Rochefoucauld, *Frenchman in England*, p. 63.

[8] Quoted "as a quip to Abraham Cooper" by Stella A. Walker, *Sporting Art: England 1700–1900* (New York: Clarkson N. Potter, 1972), p. 240.

Jaunts and Jollities (first published in periodical form, 1831–34), provides a visual equivalent to Surtees' novels in recording aristocrats and Cockney sportsmen alike in every kind of predicament, and in a wide variety of sports.

The eighteenth century also saw the beginnings of organised shooting, the rearing and preserving of game birds, and the stringent enforcement of laws against poachers. Alken's *National Sports of Great Britain*, 1821, included illustrations not only of racing, fox-hunting, stag-hunting, and coursing, but also of shooting grouse, partridge, pheasant, snipe, water hen, wild fowl, and bittern, making Robert Wilkinson Padley's *Winter Gull* (catalogue no. 32) seem not unusual game. Coursing and cricket clubs were founded, fishing and archery societies formed, boxing and fencing academies established, prize-fights and cock-fights staged.

The systematic breeding of the thoroughbred horse, the foxhound, and farm livestock encouraged proud owners to want portraits of famous sires and prize-winning cattle or sheep, like the *Two Durham Oxen*, raised to prodigious weight and slaughtered to celebrate a Staffordshire baronet's coming of age (catalogue no. 29). There was what Thomas Bewick called a "*rage* for fat Cattle, fed up to so great a weight & bulk as it was possible for feeding to make them; but this was not enough; they were to be figured monstrously fat before the owners of them could be pleased." He "objected to put lumps of fat here and there where I could not see it," and failed to please some patrons.[9] Thomas Weaver's *Two Durham Oxen* are depicted comparatively realistically, the only exaggeration being in the diminutive size of the cocks and hens who share their farmyard. William Williams's *Farm Scenes* (catalogue nos. 30, 31) have considerable documentary value, as well as great charm (but is the setting England or America?). George Morland's *Pigs and Piglets in a Sty* has little charm but immense realism (catalogue no. 22).

[9] Iain Bain, ed., *Memoir of Thomas Bewick written by himself* (1975), p. 141.

Coaching and driving provided sporting artists with abundant subject-matter. Thomas de Quincey was not alone in admiring "the absolute perfection of all the appointments about the carriages and the harness, their strength, the brilliant cleanliness, their beautiful simplicity—but more than all, the royal magnificence of the horses."[10] Although racehorses and hunters provided most of his subjects, Ben Marshall also painted coach-horses; his portrait of *David, the Property of Henry Villebois Esqr., with Two Other Coach-Horses*, like R. B. Davis's *Portraits of Old Carriage-Horses in His Late Majesty's Stud at Windsor*, reflects the majesty of the heavy horse (catalogue nos. 26 and 34). The skilful driving of coach- or carriage-horses was an aspect of horsemanship which appealed to many gentlemen, like Henry Villebois, who became enthusiastic amateurs, priding themselves on super-professional coachmanship and immaculate turn-out. Artists who had known coaching in its prime continued to provide a nostalgic public with coaching scenes long after the railways had replaced mail- and stage-coaches.

Most people could afford to buy sporting pictures only in the form of prints, like Mr. Jorrocks, in whose dining room "Candles in the hands of bronze Dianas on the marble mantlepiece lighted up a coloured copy of John Warde on Blue Ruin, while Mr. Ralph Lambton, on his horse Undertaker, with his hounds and men, occupied a frame on the opposite wall."[11] Between 1775 and 1850, several thousand sporting prints were published. Within that period, the supply must have seemed endless; but few original issues have survived in good condition. Many were pinned up unglazed in taverns, or cut up to make scrap-books or varnished screens. To publishers of sporting prints, the perfection of the aquatint pro-

[10] "The English Mail-Coach" in *Works by Thomas de Quincey*, vol. 4 (n.p., n.d.), p. 311.
[11] Robert Smith Surtees, *John Jorrocks's Jaunts & Jollities*, ed. Joseph Grego (n.p., n.d.), p. 240.

cess by the end of the eighteenth century must have seemed providential, for it was the ideal medium for translating sporting paintings and drawings into prints. The sharply etched outlines and graduated tones of aquatints coloured by hand gave them the semblance of watercolour drawings. That was how James Pollard began his career, "making drawings, designs for engravers and etching outlines to be aquatinted in imitation of drawings."[12] Artists who worked regularly for publishers had to work hard and against time to ensure that their work could be engraved in time for publication to be topical.

Francis Grant's large painting *The Melton Hunt Going to Draw the Ram's Head Cover*, one of the grandest salutes ever made to foxhunting, takes this collection up to 1839 (catalogue no. 58). Its setting is the Leicestershire countryside near Melton Mowbray, once an obscure market town but by 1839 the mecca for sportsmen from all over Britain. There is no doubt that it was Grant's accurate portraiture of socially eminent people which earned the picture high praise in the *Art-Union*'s review of the Royal Academy exhibition of 1839:

This work is an epic of its class. None of what are usually called "sporting pictures," of which the last century has been so fertile, are for a moment to be compared with it. Mr. Grant is an admirable artist, and he perfectly understands that of which we know nothing—the mystery of horses, hounds and huntsmen, and all matters thereunto appertaining. This subject includes no fewer than thirty-six portraits, including a larger proportion of the aristocratic Nimrods of the day.[13]

The reviewer added—and in that intensely snobbish age it was the final accolade—"It has been, we understand, purchased by the Duke of Wellington."

Grant's painting includes a portrait of the Marquis of Waterford, also portrayed (though more sketchily) by F. C. Turner (catalogue nos. 36–39). Grant shows him out with the celebrated Quorn Hunt, in what was usually reckoned to be the best hunting country in England. At home in Ireland, the Marquis hunted in Tipperary, and when arsonists destroyed the kennels and stables there, he had to content himself with hunting at home in county Waterford. Like a good sportsman, he did not complain. His sister-in-law, however, observed: "Hunting in this country must be very bad, from the very accounts they bring home of good runs, and Waterford's delight when he gets one. It is rocky, stony ground, often mountainous and boggy, but as Waterford has a taste for difficulties, he finds an interest in them and is not likely to be disheartened."[14]

Francis Grant was the only painter of sporting pictures to become President of the Royal Academy and to be knighted (though it must be admitted that these honours were in recognition of his portraiture rather than his sporting pictures), but he was by no means the only painter of sport who was himself a sportsman. Most of the artists represented here were sportsmen, and they noted details with an expert's eye—fortunately, for the details of how a rider sits in the saddle, how a good shot handles his gun, or how a team of horses is put to a carriage, had to be accurately observed and realistically painted.

Henry Alken rode to hounds and had a particularly sharp eye for good and bad horsemanship, demonstrating, with infinite variations, the imbalance between *Qualified Horses and Unqualified Sportsmen*, whether the latter were tradesmen or the snobs and thrusters of Melton.[15] James Barenger bred pointers; R. B. Davis,

---

[12] Quoted by N. C. Selway, *The Golden Age of Coaching and Sport* (Leigh-on-Sea, England: F. Lewis, 1972), p. 10.

[13] *Art-Union, A Monthly Journal of Fine Arts* 1 (1839): 70–71.

[14] Augustus J. C. Hare, *The Story of Two Noble Lives*, vol. 1 (London and Orpington: G. Allen; New York: D. F. Randolph & Co., 1893), p. 276.

[15] *Qualified Horses and Unqualified Sportsmen* is the title of a print series by Henry Alken.

whose brother Charles was Huntsman to the Royal Buckhounds, often followed the royal packs on foot, making rough sketches which he later worked up into paintings. Ben Marshall wrote racing reports under the pseudonym "Observator" for the *Sporting Magazine*. The obituary for Abraham Cooper in that magazine described him as an all-round sportsman who "rode to hounds, was a good shot and a particularly clever fly-fisherman." James Pollard's favorite diversion was fishing. He was a meticulous painter and draughtsman of coaching incidents and accidents, and, like Ben Marshall, had himself experienced a coaching accident. The family diary of July 1836 records that he was "thrown off a stage at Walham Green on his way to Goodwood Races by the horses running away and overturning the coach. Several passengers had their limbs broken, but J. P. escaped with a strained back."[16] John Frederick Herring started his career as night coachman on the Doncaster mail-coach and later retired to the Kentish countryside, where he could paint farm animals and rural scenes to his heart's content. Sir Francis Grant was said never to have allowed his work to interfere with fox-hunting. In his self-portrait as President of the Royal Academy, he sports a fox's head in pink coral on his black silk cravat, and he characteristically elected to be buried in Melton Mowbray.

Paul Mellon has declared that "British sporting art has always, blindly and mistakenly, been grossly underrated."[17] He has done more than any other individual to convince curators and critics that sporting pictures are an aspect of British art which deserves its place in museum collections not merely for its documentary value but in its own right. As well as his gifts and continued support to the Yale Center for British Art, Mr. Mellon presented thirty sporting paintings to the Tate Gallery in London in 1979. His gift to Virginia, where hounds have been kept since the 1660s and where quarter-mile races have been run since the 1670s, ensures that outside his own, the finest and most comprehensive collection of British sporting art in America or England will be in the Virginia Museum of Fine Arts.

JUDY EGERTON

[16] Selway, *Golden Age*, p. 16.

[17] Excerpt from "A Collector Recollects," a speech delivered by Paul Mellon at the opening of the exhibition *Painting in England 1700–1850* at the Virginia Museum of Fine Arts, April 20, 1963, published in *Selected Paintings, Drawings, and Books* (New Haven: Yale University, 1977), p. xii.

The Catalogue

2 *A Bay Horse Got by the Leedes Arabian*, ca. 1715

Oil on canvas, 99 x 124.5 (39 x 49)

Inscribed, lower left: *J Wootton*; lettered on a wall beneath a coat of arms, upper left: *This Horse was Bred / by M^r: Leeds A York / Shire Gentleman / & Call'd By his / Name*

Acc. No. 85.458

The Leedes Arabian was imported into England in the late seventeenth century and was acquired by Edward Leedes of North Millforth, Yorkshire. Wootton's painting must portray one of the progeny of the Leedes Arabian rather than that horse itself. Wootton's portrait of *The Leedes Arabian* deliberately includes a groom in Arabian dress to indicate that the horse was bred and reared in Arabia.[2] The setting in *A Bay Horse Got by the Leedes Arabian* perhaps represents Wootton's idea of Yorkshire where, according to the inscription, this horse was bred; otherwise, the composition is basically the same as in *A Bay Horse Led Towards a Rubbing-Down House at Newmarket* (catalogue no. 1), and in many other racehorse portraits by Wootton.

REFERENCES: Egerton, *Mellon Collection*, p. 12, no. 14.
COLLECTIONS: Lieutenant-Colonel R.F.A. Sloane-Stanley; sold Christie's February 25, 1949; bought by Arthur Ackermann & Son Ltd.; acquired 1960.

[2] Lady Wentworth, *The Authentic Arabian Horse* (1962), pl. 10.

4

This Horse was Bred
by Mr. Leeds, A York
shire Gentleman,
& Call'd By his
Name.

CATALOGUE ENTRY 2

3 A Nobleman Arriving to Inspect Racehorses at Newmarket, ca. 1735

Oil on canvas, 67.3 x 117.1 ($26^{1}/_{2}$ x $46^{1}/_{8}$)

Acc. No. 85.459

A companion picture entitled *Lord Portmore Watching Racehorses at Exercise on Newmarket Heath*, now in the Yale Center for British Art, portrays Charles Colyear, second Lord Portmore (1700–1785), who was devoted to racing, owned many famous horses, and superintended the management of the royal racehorses.[3] *A Nobleman Arriving to Inspect Racehorses at Newmarket* may also portray Lord Portmore, wearing the Star of the Order of the Thistle which he was awarded in 1732.

There were several rubbing-down houses on Newmarket Heath in the eighteenth century; this one, invariably shown in Wootton's paintings with four doorways and at the Newmarket town end of the course, appears to have been reserved for those connected with the King's stables.

REFERENCES: Egerton, *Mellon Collection*, p. 25, no. 26 (listing earlier reproductions).
COLLECTIONS: Rev. E. H. Dawkins; sold Christie's February 28, 1913 (no. 46); bought by Knoedler; Earl of Derby, M.C.; sold Christie's April 2, 1971 (no. 93).

[3] Judy Egerton, *The Paul Mellon Collection, British Sporting and Animal Paintings 1655–1867* (London: The Tate Gallery for the Yale Center for British Art, 1978), p. 24, no. 25, pl. 8.

CATALOGUE ENTRY 3

Painter of small conversation pieces and scenes of town and country life, in a style deriving from Teniers. Born in Dunkirk; died in Rennes. From 1716 to 1728 Angellis lived in London, in Covent Garden, the subject of several of his pictures. Ellis Waterhouse describes his pictures as "extremely neat and prevailingly light in tone." [4]

 ## *A Game of Skittles*, 1727

Oil on canvas, 63.5 x 74.5 (25 x 29⁵/₁₆)
Inscribed, lower center: *P Angellis 1727*
Acc. No. 85.460

This game appears to be an impromptu one, taking place in the garden of a country inn; on the left are the inn-keeper, in his apron, and a player about to bowl from an improbably close angle. Nowadays the game would more correctly be called "ninepins," which was often played in the garden or alley of an inn; in skittles, a variation of ninepins, the pins are set in a wooden-framed square and the game is usually played indoors. Both ninepins and skittles were traditionally associated with sociable drinking. "Life is not all beer and skittles" is a common English saying, probably deriving from George Crabbe's comment on "All the joys that ale and skittles give," in his poem *The Paris Register*, 1807.

COLLECTIONS: Anonymous sale, Sotheby's, July 19, 1978 (no. 8, illus.), attributed to Joseph van Aken; bought by Richard Green, whose restoration revealed the painting's signature and date; acquired 1979.

[4] Ellis Waterhouse, *Paintings in Britain: 1530–1790*, 2nd ed. (Baltimore: Penguin Books, 1962).

CATALOGUE ENTRY 4

A sporting artist, born in London, the son of James Seymour, goldsmith at the sign of the Flower de Luce, Fleet Street. The elder Seymour was an amateur artist, collector and possibly dealer in pictures and prints, and, like Wootton, a member of the Society of Virtuosi of St. Luke. The younger James Seymour may well have been self-taught and studied works in his father's collection. He probably knew Wootton and worked frequently at Newmarket. His oil paintings are somewhat formalized; many of his racing, hunting, and stable scenes are engraved. Contemporary sources note Seymour's genius and spirit for drawing horses. Accounts of the artist's prodigal career spent in pursuit of racing, gaming, and women are difficult to reconcile with his prolific output. He had many imitators, and apparently at least one pupil, Thomas Spencer.

5 *Mr. Peter Delmé's Hounds on the Hampshire Downs*, 1738

Oil on canvas, 101.5 x 127 (40 x 50)
Inscribed lower right: *J. Seymour - /fecit 1738*. A label (ca. 1800?) verso is inscribed *This picture belonged to Lady Ravensworth. The Hounds are her Father's* [an error for her brother's] *Mr. Delmé—The Figures all Portraits. Scene in Hampshire.*
Acc. No. 85.508

Against a background of green hills, eight riders move off in a group from the right behind the huntsman and hounds. Although the inscription states that the figures are "all Portraits," they can no longer be identified. However, Peter Delmé himself is presumably the young man on a chestnut horse who leans forward to listen attentively to the rider on a grey preceding him.

Peter Delmé (1710–1770) was the eldest son of Sir Peter Delmé (1667–1728), Governor of the Bank of England 1715–17 and Lord Mayor of London in 1723. The younger Peter Delmé lived the life of a country gentleman in Hampshire; his sister married Lord Ravensworth in 1733. Peter Delmé's enthusiasm for hunting was transmitted through several generations; his family's riding skills are noted by the sporting writer "Nimrod" (C. J. Apperley). F. P. Delmé Radcliffe, author of the hunting classic *The Noble Science* and Master of the Hertfordshire Hunt 1835–39 (painted by James Pollard, catalogue nos. 50–53), was the great-grandson of the Peter Delmé painted by Seymour.

REFERENCES: Roger Longrigg, *The History of Foxhunting* (London: MacMillan, 1975), p. 84, illus.; Egerton, *Mellon Collection*, pp. 42–43, no. 45, pl. 16.
COLLECTIONS: Painted for Peter Delmé; his sister, Lady Ravensworth; Duke of Grafton by 1890; Oscar & Peter Johnson; acquired 1969.
EXHIBITIONS: Grosvenor Gallery, *Works of Art illustrative of and connected with Sport*, 1890 (no. 44); Oscar & Peter Johnson, Lowndes Lodge Gallery, *Sport and the Horse*, 1969 (no. 44, illus.); Yale Center for British Art, *Noble Exercise, The Sporting Ideal in Eighteenth-Century British Art*, 1982 (no. 19, illus.).

CATALOGUE ENTRY 5

Ross is so far known only from paintings of hunting scenes signed and dated between 1729 and 1732; nothing is known of his life.

 A Meet of Foxhounds, 1732

Oil on canvas, 102.2 x 126.7 (40¼ x 49⅞)

Inscribed, lower left: *J. Ross / 1732*

Acc. No. 85.461

The hounds—one scratching itself, one lifting its leg, one making off towards newly-arrived riders, others in various attitudes—are realistically portrayed. The setting is hilly country, near an estuary or sea-coast overlooked by a large curiously shaped rock in the background on the left. The rock formation was identified as "The Prating Rock, Somerset" when the picture was sold in 1969 and exhibited in 1971, though no rock of this name or shape is now known in Somerset.

REFERENCES: Egerton, *Mellon Collection*, pp. 50–51, no. 53, pl. 19.
COLLECTIONS: Geoffrey Clapham, sold Sotheby's March 12, 1969 (no. 106, illus.); bought by Thomas Agnew & Sons Ltd.; acquired 1971.
EXHIBITIONS: Thomas Agnew & Sons Ltd., *English Life and Landscape 1730–1870*, 1971 (no. 6, illus.); Yale Center for British Art, *Noble Exercise, The Sporting Ideal in Eighteenth-Century British Art*, 1982 (no. 15).

CATALOGUE ENTRY 6

A painter of horses. Spencer's life and career are so far obscure. Vertue calls him "a scholar" of James Seymour, to whom perhaps much of Spencer's unsigned work has been attributed.[5] Certainly Spencer worked in Seymour's manner, but he lacks Seymour's originality. He is believed to have been one of the artists employed by Thomas Butler of Pall Mall, who advertised in contemporary newspapers his readiness to supply sporting pictures. Some of Spencer's work was engraved, with Seymour's, in a series of portraits of racehorses published in the 1740s and 1750s.

7 *Sir Edward Marshall Riding a Chestnut Horse,* 1752

Oil on canvas, 63.5 x 76.2 (25 x 30)
Inscribed lower left: *T Spencer / Pin.ˣ 1752*
Acc. No. 85.462

An old label on the back of the frame reads: *Sir Edward Marshall of Surrey, known / as "The Sporting Baronet" / T. Spencer 1751 [sic]*. The sitter has not yet been further identified. The label seems to be in error in describing the sitter as a baronet; the name of Sir Edward Marshall is not included in G. E. Cokayne's comprehensive *Complete Baronetage*. Possibly Sir Edward Marshall was a knight rather than a baronet, but his name cannot be traced by the Surrey County archivist. The coat of arms included in the upper right of the painting may provide a clue for further research.

COLLECTIONS: Peter Weeks, Inc., Middleburg, Virginia; acquired 1984.

[5] Vertue, *MS Notes*.

GEORGE STUBBS, Associate of the Royal Academy (1724–1806)

A painter of horses and dogs; wild animals sometimes depicted in combat; sporting scenes, portraits, and conversation pieces; an engraver; an anatomist; and a technical experimenter. Born in Liverpool, the son of a currier, Stubbs briefly assisted the copyist Hamlet Winstanley at Knowsley Hall but is otherwise self-taught. Stubbs is believed to have first worked as a portrait painter in Liverpool, Leeds, Hull, and York. Meanwhile, he studied anatomy at York and designed and etched illustrations for Dr. John Burton's Essay towards a Complete New System of Midwifery, *1751. In Lincolnshire in 1756, he began intensive research into the anatomy of the horse, dissecting, observing, and then delineating from the skin to the skeleton in masterly drawings which he engraved and published as* The Anatomy of the Horse, *1766. By 1760 he had settled in London, where he soon established his reputation. His patrons included the Duke of Richmond and the Earl of Grosvenor; one of his works was purchased by Sir Joshua Reynolds. Stubbs exhibited at the Society of Artists, 1761–74, for which he served as director, treasurer, and finally president in 1772, and at the Royal Academy, 1775–1803, to which he was elected associate in 1780. He failed to qualify for full membership because he did not deposit a diploma picture. He experimented with enamel painting, first on copper, then on Wedgwood tablets. By combining methods of mezzotint, etching, and engraving, he produced some expert engravings of his own work. Stubbs is the most original and searching of all sporting and animal painters. His sense of design is almost always assured, and the balance between tension and naturalism in his work is matchless.*

 Black and White Spaniel Following a Scent, 1773

Oil on canvas, 63.5 x 76 (25 x 30)
Inscribed lower right: *Geo: Stubbs pinxit / 1773*
Acc. No. 85.506

A black and white spaniel paws its way towards the left, its head partly turned to the front, its nose to the ground as it follows a scent. Visible on the left are spindly trees; in the distance beyond them, a remote view of a substantial white house.

The picture possibly was painted for the second Earl of Clarendon, though he was only twenty in 1773. He became an important patron in the last years of Stubbs's life and may have acquired the picture later. The white house in the background is not the Earl's seat, The Grove, Watford.

Stubbs used a closely similar nose-to-the-ground pose for portraits of at least two other spaniels, with different markings and backgrounds: one, a picture of similar dimensions, with Knoedler ca. 1930; the other, a smaller panel dated 1777, exhibited by Richard Green, 1968 (illus. frontispiece, in colour).

REFERENCES: Egerton, *Mellon Collection*, p. 86, no. 83.
COLLECTIONS: Second Earl of Clarendon (?) ; by descent to the sixth Earl of Clarendon; sold Christie's February 13, 1920 (no. 101); bought by Hon. Geoffrey Lawrence; sold Christie's February 26, 1926 (no. 23); bought by Urquhart; Mrs. Cox; sold Bonham's February 6, 1964 (no. 197); Agnew; acquired 1964.
EXHIBITIONS: Royal Academy, *Paintings in England 1700–1850 from the Collection of Mr. and Mrs. Paul Mellon*, 1964–65 (no. 291).

Sporting and portrait painter; exhibited at the Society of Artists and Free Society, 1761–65. His subjects include horses, dogs, dead game, and portraits. Edward Edwards remarked that Roper's "powers as an artist were not considerable, yet sufficient to satisfy the gentlemen of the turf and stable."[6]

9 *The Match Between Driver and Aaron at Maidenhead August 1754: Driver Winning the First Heat,*

ca. 1754

Oil on canvas, 89 x 122 (35 x 48)

Inscribed, lower left: *R. Roper pinx^t*; below subject: *DRIVER and AARON, Running the first heat at Maidenhead, August 1754. / DRIVER was Rode by Thos: Brett AARON by Sam: Tate, both Horses fell at comeing in, Drivers Rider was hurt with the fall, Driver had the heat*

Acc. No. 85.463.

This is the first in a set of three paintings depicting the three heats run in a match between Mr. Lamego's chestnut horse, Driver, and Mr. Rogers's bay horse, Aaron. Driver won the first heat, Aaron the second, and the match was decided by Driver's victory in the third heat. In each of the three pictures the two horses gallop towards a finishing post on the left, whipped on by their jockeys. The picture of *Aaron Winning the Second Heat* remains in Paul Mellon's collection. *Driver Winning the Third Heat* was presented by Paul Mellon to the Tate Gallery through the British Sporting Art Trust in 1979 (no. T 02371, illustrated in the *Tate Gallery Illustrated Catalogue of Acquisitions 1978–80*, 1981, p. 38).

REFERENCES: Egerton, *Mellon Collection*, p. 110, no. 105 (1).
COLLECTIONS: As one of a set of three, anonymous sale Sotheby's, July 25, 1928 (no. 99); bought by Lambert; Arthur Ackermann & Son Ltd., 1929; Jack Gilbey Ellis; acquired 1970.
EXHIBITIONS: Arthur Ackermann & Son Ltd., *British Sporting Artists*, 1929 (106, no. 1); Yale Center for British Art, *Noble Exercise, The Sporting Ideal in Eighteenth-Century British Art*, 1982 (no. 37, p. 19).

6 Edward Edwards, *Anecdotes of Painters who have resided or been born in England* (London: Leigh and Sotheby, 1808).

DRIVER and AARON, Running the first heat at Maidenhead, August 1754.
DRIVER was Rode by Thos Brett AARON by Sam Tate, both Horses fell at comeing in, Drivers Rider was hurt with the fall, Driver had the heat

CATALOGUE ENTRY 9

10

A Hunter Held by a Stable-Boy for His Master, 1762

Oil on canvas, 130.5 x 180.25 (51³/4 x 71)

Inscribed, lower left: *R.Roper Pinxᵗ / 1762*

Acc. No. 85.464

The identification of the gentleman who commissioned his portrait on such a large scale is now unknown, but no doubt he, his horse, and his stable-boy are all portrayed from life. The skins of two dead foxes pinned on the stable wall are presumably trophies from earlier hunts.

REFERENCES: Egerton, *Mellon Collection*, p. 110, no. 106.
COLLECTIONS: Arthur Ackermann & Son Ltd.; acquired 1966.
EXHIBITIONS: Arthur Ackermann & Son Ltd., *Annual Exhibition of Fine XVIIIth & XIXth Century Sporting Paintings*, 1965 (no. 24, illus.).

CATALOGUE ENTRY 10

PHILIP REINAGLE, Royal Academician (1749–1833)

*Sporting, natural history, portrait, and landscape painter; born in Scotland
(?), son of a Hungarian bandsman. Studied at the Royal Academy Schools
and exhibited regularly at the Royal Academy and British Institution,
1773–1832; elected Royal Academician in 1812. Several of his children
became artists. Died in London.*

11 *Portrait of an Extraordinary Musical Dog,*
exhibited 1805

Oil on canvas, 72 x 92.5 (28¼ x 36½)
Acc. No. 85.465

The dog's paws rest on the keyboard; a musical score (made up with
considerable artistic licence) is open before him, and apparently execu-
tion is about to commence. There appear to be no records of the per-
formances of an "extraordinary musical dog"; *The Times, The Gentleman's
Magazine,* and *The Sporting Magazine* have been searched in vain. The
subject is, however, likely to be real rather than imaginary. Reinagle is
known to have been specially interested in spaniels and the extent to
which they could be trained.

REFERENCES: Egerton, *Mellon Collection*, p. 145, no. 137.
COLLECTIONS: St. Clair Ford, 1878; Frank T. Sabin; acquired 1966.
EXHIBITIONS: Royal Academy, 1805 (no. 259).

CATALOGUE ENTRY II

THOMAS GOOCH (ca. 1750–last exhibited 1802)

Sporting and animal painter, probably a pupil of Sawrey Gilpin, from whose address he first exhibited at the Society of Artists, 1778–80. His seventy-six exhibits at the Royal Academy, 1781–1802, included paintings of carriage-horses, hunters, dogs, various animals, and equestrian portraits.

12 *A Gentleman with His Horse and Dogs*, 1780

Oil on canvas, 63 x 91.5 (24³/4 x 36)

Inscribed, lower right: *T : Gooch / 1780*

Acc. No. 85.466

Gooch used the same composition the following year for a portrait of *Matthew Howard with His Hunter in the Grounds of His Hunting-Lodge at Beulah Hill*, signed and dated 1781, possibly the picture exhibited at the Royal Academy in 1781 (no. 29) and now in the collection of Thomas G. Wyman, New York. Matthew Howard perhaps admired the relaxed and informal poses of the earlier picture and commissioned his own portrait in a similar attitude.

REFERENCES: Egerton, *Mellon Collection*, p. 147, no. 140.
COLLECTIONS: Frank T. Sabin; acquired 1966.
EXHIBITIONS: (?) the picture of this title at the Society of Artists, 1780 (no. 101).

CATALOGUE ENTRY 12

Leicestershire-born painter of horses and cattle; studied at the Royal Academy Schools; exhibited 1776–88, mostly portraits of hunters. Evidently he admired the work of George Stubbs, because he made some signed copies of Stubbs's paintings.

13 *A Roan Hunter Waiting with a Hunt Servant, a Foxhound and a Terrier*, ca. 1780–1800

Oil on canvas, 72 x 91.5 (28¼ x 36)
Acc. No. 85.467

The hunter, a flecked roan, waits already saddled for his master, his reins held by a hunt servant in an unidentified livery of scarlet coat and blue collar. The solid yet rather ungainly poses are characteristic of Boultbee's work.

REFERENCES: Egerton, *Mellon Collection*, p. 150, no. 146, pl. 53.
COLLECTIONS: Anonymous sale Sotheby's March 23, 1966 (no. 96, illus.).

CATALOGUE ENTRY 13

Only son of the sporting painter Francis Sartorius, and presumably his pupil; became a prolific sporting painter but lacked his father's individuality. Exhibited 1776–1824. His subjects, chiefly hunting and racing scenes, also include some coach-horses, dogs and cattle, and versions of earlier artists' work. Father of John Francis, sporting painter, and Francis, marine painter.

14 - 17 *Fox-hunting*, a set of four, 1787

Setting out
Full Cry
Gone Away
The Kill

Oil on canvas, average size 35.5 x 48.5 (14 x 19$^{1}/_{16}$)

Inscribed, lower right, nos. 14 and 17; lower left, no. 15: *J N Sartorius pinx. 1787.*

Acc. Nos. 85.468.1/4

COLLECTIONS: Henry Blyth; Mrs. David Partridge; Leggatt Brothers; acquired 1978.

CATALOGUE ENTRY 14

CATALOGUE ENTRY 15

CATALOGUE ENTRY 16

CATALOGUE ENTRY 17

18 *The Death of the Fox,* ca. 1800

Oil on canvas, 96.5 x 122 (38 x 48)

Inscribed indistinctly, lower left: *J N Sartorius*; and on a label verso: *"Nimrod" a famous Hunter the property / of Joseph Hay Esqr / New Grove Lancashire*

Acc. No. 85.469

REFERENCES: Egerton, *Mellon Collection*, p. 158, no. 153.
COLLECTIONS: Sir Walter Gilbey, Bart.; sold Christie's March 12, 1910 (no. 132); bought by Leggatt Brothers; F. Ambrose Clark; Mrs. Stephen Clark Jr.; Thomas Agnew & Sons Ltd.; acquired 1968.
EXHIBITIONS: Grosvenor Gallery, *Sports and Arts*, 1890–91 (no. 49).

CATALOGUE ENTRY 18

19-20 *Fox-hunting in Wooded Country*, a pair, ca.
1800
Breaking Cover
The Death

Oil on canvas, 55 x 76.2 (21³/₄ x 30)

Inscribed, lower left, no. 19: *J N Sartorius Pinx. 18*[??]; lower right, no. 20: *J N Sartorius pinx.*

Acc. Nos. 85.470.1/2

REFERENCES: Egerton, *Mellon Collection*, p. 158, no. 154.
COLLECTIONS: Arthur Ackermann & Son Ltd.; acquired 1960.
EXHIBITIONS: Virginia Museum of Fine Arts, *Painting in England 1700–1850: Collection of Mr. & Mrs. Paul Mellon*, 1963 (nos. 342, 341).

CATALOGUE ENTRY 19

GEORGE GARRARD, Associate of the Royal Academy
(1760–1826)

Painter of animals, landscapes, genre scenes, and agricultural life; modeller of animals and portrait busts. Studied under Sawrey Gilpin and in the Royal Academy Schools. Exhibited regularly at the Royal Academy and British Institution, 1783–1825; elected Associate of the Royal Academy, 1800. Many of his paintings are of high quality.

21 *A Barbary Antelope and a Black Swan from New Holland,* 1811

Oil on canvas, 76.25 x 94 (30 x 37)

Inscribed on the stretcher: *A Barbary Antelope & a Black Swan from New Holland / painted by George Garrard A R A October 1811*

Acc. No. 85.471

Presumably these are creatures separately observed in a menagerie, then combined in a romantic composition in which the tawny antelope rears up at the approach of a majestic black swan of apparently almost the same size. The sky is dark and stormy, as if presaging combat, which in this case is hardly likely, but the representation of different species as potential if not actual combatants was common among painters of wild animals.

REFERENCES: Egerton, *Mellon Collection*, pp. 165–66, no. 164.
COLLECTIONS: The Earl of Ilchester; Frank T. Sabin; acquired 1967.

CATALOGUE ENTRY 21

Sporting, animal, and genre painter. Born in London, son of the portraitist Henry Morland, to whom he was apprenticed; later studied at the Royal Academy Schools, first exhibiting "Sketches" at the Royal Academy at the age of ten, and continuing to exhibit until 1804. Morland married Anne Ward, sister of the artists William and James Ward. By 1787, he had established a reputation for elegant and sentimental genre scenes, gradually changing in the 1790s to earthier rustic subjects: cart-horses in stables, farm animals (notably pigs), village laborers, etc. He kept pigs, poultry, and rabbits in his studio as models. Numerous engravings after his work include sixty-nine by his brother-in-law William Ward. Morland's life became riotously debauched, and he was often drunk, in debt, and in flight from his creditors. The quality of his work declined as he tossed off pictures to raise money; he died aged forty-one.

22 *Pigs and Piglets in a Sty*, ca. 1800

Oil on canvas, 24 x 30.5 (9$\frac{1}{2}$ x 12)
Inscribed, lower left: *G.M^d.*
Acc. No. 85.472

Morland liked pigs and enjoyed painting them; several of his other studies of pigs were engraved. As Ellis Waterhouse remarks, Morland comes "very close to the heart of common things," notably in "the piggishness of his pigs."[7]

REFERENCES: Egerton, *Mellon Collection*, p. 172, no. 172.
COLLECTIONS: Spink & Son Ltd.; acquired 1963.

[7] Waterhouse, *Paintings in Britain*, p. 224.

CATALOGUE ENTRY 22

23 *A Winter Landscape with Skaters on a Frozen Stream*, ca. 1800

Oil on canvas, 26.5 x 31.5 (10³/₈ x 12³/₈)

Acc. No. 85.473

An identical version was sold at Sotheby's March 23, 1964 (no. 44, illus.). Morland often repeated subjects which had proven popular.

COLLECTIONS: Anonymous sale, Sotheby's January 17, 1962 (no. 193).
EXHIBITIONS: Virginia Museum of Fine Arts, *Painting in England 1700–1850: Collection of Mr. & Mrs. Paul Mellon*, 1963 (no. 50, pl. 137).

CATALOGUE ENTRY 23

24

A Woodland Scene, Going to Market, ca. 1800

Oil on panel, 32.25 x 41 (12³/₄ x 16¹/₈)

Inscribed in red, on saddlebag: *GM*

Acc. No. 85.474

COLLECTIONS: Alphaus Morhange, sold Sotheby's March 18, 1964 (no. 124).

CATALOGUE ENTRY 24

JOHN CORDREY (ca. 1765–ca. 1825)

Sporting painter of naive but engaging style. Cordrey's life and career are obscure, but he presumably was self-taught and possibly began as a coach painter. He specialized in coaching scenes and painted occasional hunting pictures and portraits of horses.

25   *Fox-hunting: Full Cry*, 1819

Oil on canvas, 53.3 x 76.5 (21 x 30⅛)

Inscribed, lower left: *Cordrey Pinx! / 1819*

Acc. No. 85.475

REFERENCES: Egerton, *Mellon Collection*, pp. 178–79, no. 182.
COLLECTIONS: Dr. A. L. Crockford; sold Sotheby's July 17, 1974 (no. 169, illus.); bought by Arthur Ackermann & Son Ltd.; acquired 1975.
EXHIBITIONS: Arthur Ackermann & Son Ltd., *Annual Exhibition of Sporting Paintings*, 1974 (no. 5).

CATALOGUE ENTRY 25

Sporting painter, born in Leicestershire; studied briefly under the portrait painter Lemuel Francis Abbott. Frequently worked at Newmarket, and settled near there 1812–25. As an "Honorary Exhibitor" he showed thirteen paintings at the Royal Academy, 1801–19, but his work was chiefly known to his contemporaries through sixty engravings, mostly by his friend John Scott, published in The Sporting Magazine, *1796–1832. Almost all of Marshall's subjects were sporting: chiefly racing and hunting scenes, with some shooting pictures, game cocks, etc. A genial and unaffected man, he was particularly successful as a portraitist of jockeys, trainers, boxers, and vets— energetic self-reliant men whom he could portray without the airs and graces of gentility. His pupils included his son Lambert Marshall, John Ferneley, and Abraham Cooper.*

26 David, the Property of Henry Villebois Esq.ʳ, with Two Other Coach-Horses, 1802

Oil on canvas, 85 x 99 (33¹/₂ x 39)

Inscribed, lower left: *B. Marshall pˣ / 1802*

Acc. No. 85.476

The bay horse, David, stands facing right in a stable-yard; another coach-horse is behind him, a third emerges from the stable, and presumably a fourth will also emerge to make up a team of four. In Scott's engraving, the background includes a coach-house, its doors standing open to show a private drag. The engraving was used by the anonymous author of an article on "The Coach Horse" published in *The Sportsman's Repository*, 1820, to illustrate his point that modern improvements in breeding have enhanced the elegant appearance of the draught horse without diminishing its effective power: "The Coach Horses of former days were comparatively Dray horses; those of the present wear the semblance of Hunters and Racers." Marshall's picture, the author noted, "represents one of our highest and most fashionable forms of the Coach Horse, trimmed with respect to tail and mane, and harnessed in the prevailing style of the gay and splendid metropolis."

Henry Villebois (1778?–1847) was an enthusiastic driving amateur and a founder of the very chic Benson Driving Club, whose members prided themselves on super-professional coachmanship and immaculate turn-out. Villebois was one of Marshall's regular patrons and commissioned portraits of his hunters, hacks, and carriage-horses.

REFERENCES: Egerton, *Mellon Collection*, pp. 195–96, no. 206.
COLLECTIONS: Commissioned by Henry Villebois(?); D. Skinner, Norfolk; Arthur Ackermann & Son Ltd.; acquired 1966.
ENGRAVING: By John Scott, entitled *Coach-Horse, A Portrait of David, the Property of Henry Villebois Esq.ʳ, to whom this plate is respectfully dedicated,* published in John Lawrence, *The History and Delineation of the Horse,* 1809, facing p. 118, and in *The Sportsman's Repository,* 1820, facing p. 25.

CATALOGUE ENTRY 26

27 *Henry Legard with His Favourite Hunters*, ca. 1825

Oil on canvas, 101.5 x 127 (40 x 50)

Inscribed lower right: *B. Marshall pinxt*

Acc. No. 85.507

Henry Legard, a slim young man fashionably dressed in a black cut-away coat, a cravat, a top hat, nankeen breeches, and top boots, stands facing the spectator in the center of the composition in a graceful pose: right hand on hip, left outstretched to caress the nose of a bay hunter that stands unsaddled behind him. Another bay hunter, with a white face, trots behind Henry Legard. Both horses face left, watching the approach of a stable-lad in a red jacket and a black cockaded hat, who holds out a sieve. The background is flat, open country, with a river or marshland on the right.

If the sitter is correctly identified as Henry Legard, the painting can hardly be earlier than 1825, though it looks earlier in style. Henry Willoughby Legard was born in 1805, the second son of Sir Thomas Legard, seventh Baronet, Royal Navy, of Garston, Yorkshire (his grandfather, Sir John Legard, sixth Baronet, was painted by Pompeo Batoni). Henry Legard served with the Ninth Lancers and is mentioned by "Nimrod" in his *Hunting Reminiscences*. Legard married Lord Middleton's sister Charlotte in 1839 and died on November 21, 1845.

REFERENCES: W. Shaw Sparrow, *British Sporting Artists* (London: John Lane, 1922), pl. 68 (as *The Squire and his Favourites*); W. Shaw Sparrow, *George Stubbs and Ben Marshall* (1929), following p. 64 (as *Henry Legard with His Favourite Hunters*); Egerton, *Mellon Collection*, p. 204, no. 217.

COLLECTIONS: Charles Romer Williams; Agnew, 1920; J. H. McFadden, Jr., 1923; Leggatt Brothers, 1927; E. J. Rousuck; acquired 1970.

Painter of domestic and wild animals, sporting scenes, landscapes, portraits, allegorical and historical pictures, with a prolific output. Born in London, son of a fruit-dealer; trained as an engraver, but increasingly preferred to paint, at first following his brother-in-law George Morland's style and subject-matter but quickly developing his own forceful and imaginative style. An ambitious artist, he sought to portray in animals a combination of physical energy and nervous excitement, and he achieved uneven but often thrilling results. He died poor and somewhat embittered.

28 Portraits of Granadillo, a Brood Mare, and Skyscraper Colt, the Property of T. Crook, Esq., 1809

Oil on canvas, 70.8 x 90.8 (27⅞ x 35¾)
Inscribed, lower right: *1809. JWard* [in monogram]
Acc. No. 85.477

Granadillo, by Fidget out of Dryad, was foaled in 1794; she is portrayed here with her colt by Skyscraper. According to C. Reginald Grundy this was "the first picture of blood horses that Ward painted."[8] Ward's Account Book shows that he sold the picture in December 1809 for £63 to Thomas Garle, one of his first and most constant patrons; framing the picture cost £3.10.0 extra. *The Sporting Magazine*, November 1826, lists Ward's most important works to date and records eight works, including this picture, in Thomas Garle's possession. Years later, on May 22, 1848, Ward wrote from retirement to Thomas Garle, recollecting the works his patron had chosen from his studio, almost certainly with this picture in his mind: "Your taste and judgment has continued to skim off the cream of my Dairy—for I should be a dissatisfied mortal indeed if not content with the powers given me in your Lioness, Mare and Foal, and the Eagle, and which will ever fly in the same atmosphere if not fly over the heads of my highest soarings in the same walk."[9]

REFERENCES: James Ward's MS. Account Book, p. 4; *Sporting Magazine* 19 (November 1826): 2; C. Reginald Grundy, *James Ward R. A.* (1909), p. 45, no. 390.
COLLECTIONS: Purchased from the artist by Thomas Garle, December 1809, for £63; thence by direct descent to Mrs. Mary Aveling of Welbury House, Northallerton, North Yorkshire; John Baskett Ltd.; acquired 1977.
EXHIBITIONS: Royal Academy, 1809 (no. 10).

[8] C. Reginald Grundy, *James Ward R.A.* (London, Otto Ltd., 1909).
[9] Ward to Garle, May 22, 1848, MS, Victoria and Albert Museum Library, London.

CATALOGUE ENTRY 28

Born in Shropshire, son of a yeoman farmer. Painter of animals and sporting scenes; apparently self-taught as an artist. Specialized in portraits of pedigree farm animals, many of which were engraved. Exhibited four pictures at the Royal Academy, 1801–09, and four at the Liverpool Academy, 1814.

29 *Two Durham Oxen*, 1827

Oil on canvas, 99 x 124.5 (39 x 49)

Inscribed, lower center: *Painted by Thos Weaver Shrewsbury . 1827*

Acc. No. 85.478

These two mighty oxen were reared for the purpose of being slaughtered to celebrate the coming of age of Sir Thomas Aston Clifford Constable, second Baronet, of Tixall in the County of Stafford, on May 3, 1827. The inscription in the engraving states: "The above oxen were descended from the Stock of Edwd Blount Esqr of Bellamore. Rear'd and Fed by Mr John Bond, of Brancott, near Stafford and Slaughtered to celebrate the coming of Age of Sir Thomas Aston Clifford Constable Bar^t on the 3rd of May 1827." Tables in the engraving give the total weight of the left beast as 2,742 pounds and of the right beast as 2,437 pounds.

Here they are portrayed standing outside a barn at Brancott, near Stafford, with a man—probably John Bond, who reared them—prodding the rump of the right-hand beast. The bantam hens in the foreground accentuate the oxen's size. The background is an extensive view looking westward across the valley of the River Sow to Stafford.

REFERENCES: Egerton, *Mellon Collection*, p. 227, no. 245, pl. 81.
COLLECTIONS: Gooden & Fox; acquired 1967.
ENGRAVING: By Charles Turner, in aquatint, published by Benjamin A. Bond, Brandcott, Staffordshire, July 29, 1828 (illustrated in D. H. Boalch, *Prints and Paintings of British Farm Livestock 1780–1910*, 1958, no. 49, pl. XIII).

CATALOGUE ENTRY 29

WILLIAM WILLIAMS (active 1802)

This artist appears to be known only by these two scenes.

30-31   *Farm Scenes*, a pair, 1802
Farm Scene in Summer
Farm Scene in Winter

Oil on panel, no. 30, 73.2 x 150.2 ($28^7/8$ x $59^1/8$); no. 31, 73 x 151 ($28^3/4$ x $59^1/2$)
Inscribed, lower right: *W Williams Pinxit / 1802*
Acc. Nos. 85.479.1/2

Enquiries at the Institute of Agricultural History and Museum of English Rural Life, University of Reading, England, were answered by Keith Robinson, who thought, from details of the weatherboarded farm buildings and the variety of stock portrayed, that the farm probably was in East Anglia, perhaps in Suffolk. One very distinctive feature Mr. Robinson pointed to was the "cornhole" on the outer wall of the central barn in the summer scene, which is apparently of a type found only in Suffolk. The probability thus appears to be that these scenes were painted in Suffolk; but the possibility that the painter and his subjects may in fact have been American cannot be discounted.

COLLECTIONS: Sabin Galleries; acquired 1963.

CATALOGUE ENTRY 30

CATALOGUE ENTRY 31

An obscure and possibly amateur artist, Padley exhibited two paintings at the Royal Academy in 1815, from a Nottinghamshire address. Entitled The Produce of a Morning's Amusement in the Co. of Nottingham *and* The Produce of an Evening's Amusement in the Co. of Notting-ham, *these pictures may well have been sporting subjects, and possibly portraits of game birds, like* A Winter Gull, *below.*

32 *A Winter Gull,* 1812

Oil on canvas, 56.5 x 73.7 (22¼ x 29)

Inscribed verso, before relining: *A Winter Gull shot upon the River Trent in 1812. Wilkinson Padley*

Acc. No. 85.480

This is an immature gull, of greyish-white plumage. The river bank on which it stands is presumably that of the Trent, which runs through Nottinghamshire.

REFERENCES: Egerton, *Mellon Collection*, p. 228, no. 247.
COLLECTIONS: Spink & Son Ltd.; acquired 1967.

Born in London, son of James Barenger, painter of insects. Sporting and animal painter. Exhibited at the Royal Academy, 1807–31. Barenger's subjects included hunt scenes, horses, dogs, cattle, and game birds. Twenty-six of his works were engraved for The Sporting Magazine.

33 *Jonathan Griffin, Huntsman to the Earl of Derby's Staghounds, on Spanker*, 1819

Oil on canvas, 91.5 x 122 (36 x 48)

Inscribed, lower left: *J Barenger / 1819*

Acc. No. 85.481

Here Jonathan Griffin is portrayed in the center foreground on his grey horse, Spanker, surrounded by six or seven couple of hounds; Jem Bullen, First Whipper-in, rides to the right in the middle distance, and in the distance on the left is a group of riders including the twelfth Earl of Derby's eldest son, Lord Stanley, and his grandson, the Honourable Edward Smith-Stanley. These identifications are lettered below the subject in the engraving noted below, which retains Jonathan Griffin's central position but brings the figures of the Stanleys into prominence and reduces the number of hounds.

The twelfth Earl of Derby (1752–1834) hunted the stag in Surrey for nearly fifty years. He annually brought a contingent of horses, hounds, and carted deer from his family seat at Knowsley, Lancashire, to the Oaks, his hunting-lodge in Surrey. An enthusiastic sportsman, in whose honour two of the classic races, the Derby and the Oaks, were named, he was aged sixty-seven at the time this picture was painted; he is not represented in it.

Jonathan Griffin worked with the Earl of Derby's staghounds for twenty-five years, first as whipper-in, then as huntsman. The sporting writer "Nimrod" (C. J. Apperley) recalls him as "all over a workman, and as cheerful a fellow to ride across a country with, as ever I got alongside of."[10]

An earlier portrait by Barenger of Jonathan Griffin as huntsman to the Earl of Derby's staghounds, dated 1813, was presented by Paul Mellon to the Tate Gallery through the British Sporting Art Trust in 1979 (no. T 02356, illustrated in the *Tate Gallery Illustrated Catalogue of Acquisitions 1978–80*, 1981, p. 3).

REFERENCES: Egerton, *Mellon Collection*, pp. 233–34, no. 252.

COLLECTIONS: Mrs. N. S. Higson; sold Christie's December 8, 1961 (no. 103); bought by Leggatt; acquired 1962.

EXHIBITIONS: Virginia Museum of Fine Arts, *Painting in England 1700–1850: Collection of Mr. & Mrs. Paul Mellon*, 1963 (no. 350, pl. 11).

ENGRAVING (with differences, see above): By R. Woodman, entitled *The Earl of Derby's Staghounds*, published by J. Griffin, Carshalton, Surrey, May 15, 1823 (illustrated in colour, F. L. Wilder, *English Sporting Prints*, 1974, p. 108, pl. 42).

[10] C. J. Apperley, *Nimrod's Hunting Reminiscences*, ed. W. Shaw Sparrow (1843; 1926), p. 150.

CATALOGUE ENTRY 33

Sporting and animal painter. The son of Richard Davis, huntsman to King George III's harriers. Davis was probably initially a self-taught artist, but he attracted the attention of George III, who arranged for him to have some instruction from Sir Francis Bourgeois, Royal Academician. Royal favour continued by George IV and William IV, to each of whom he was appointed "Animal Painter," and by Queen Victoria. Thirteen works by Davis are in the Royal Collection. Exhibited regularly 1802–53. His subjects were chiefly hunters and hounds, coach-horses and cavalcades, but also included cattle fairs, some animals from literature, and The Nubian Giraffe, *painted for George IV.*

34 Portraits of Old Carriage-Horses in His Late Majesty's Stud at Windsor, 1820

Oil on canvas, 100.3 x 126.4 (39½ x 49¾)

Inscribed, lower right: *R B Davis / 1820*

Acc. No. 85.482

These dark bay carriage-horses belonged to King George III, who died on January 29, 1820. The grooms are leading them out one by one and harnessing them for carriage exercise. Davis lived at or near Windsor 1807–23 and exhibited a number of pictures of animals belonging to the royal family.

COLLECTIONS: Anonymous sale, Christie's March 27, 1981 (no. 17, illus.); bought by Spink & Son Ltd.; acquired 1983.
EXHIBITIONS: Royal Academy, 1820 (no. 133).

35 *Foxhounds in Kennels*, 1837

Oil on board, 29 x 39 (11 1/2 x 15 1/4)

Inscribed, lower left: *RB Davis*; lower right: *sketch'd / 1837*

Acc. No. 85.483

This is almost certainly a study of individual hounds in hunt kennels, made while Davis was working on a series of sixteen portraits of the hunt servants and leading hounds in particular packs, engraved as *The Hunter's Annual*, 1836–41, dedicated to William IV and Queen Victoria. In those portraits, each hound is individually named; unfortunately the hounds in this picture are not identified.

REFERENCES: Egerton, *Mellon Collection*, p. 237, no. 257.
COLLECTIONS: Leggatt Brothers, 1929; Victor Emmanuel, New York; Wildenstein, New York; acquired 1954.

sketch'd.
1837

CATALOGUE ENTRY 35

Sporting painter whose hunting, racing, steeplechasing, and shooting scenes, executed in a rather slapdash style, were very popular. Much of his work was engraved, often in sets of four or six plates, and seventy-eight engravings of his work were published in The Sporting Magazine.

36–39 *The Marquis of Waterford and Members of the Tipperary Hunt (The Noble Tips)*, a set of four, 1842

Tipperary Boys
Tipperary Melody
Tipperary Glory
Tipperary Killing, No Murder

Oil on canvas, average size 45.7 x 61 (18 x 24)

Inscribed, lower left, nos. 36, 37, 39; lower center, no. 38: *F. C. Turner 1842*

Acc. Nos. 85.484.1/4

Henry de la Poer Beresford, third Marquis of Waterford, Ireland (1811–1859), was passionately devoted to fox-hunting. As a young man he hunted chiefly with the Meltonians in Leicestershire (Francis Grant's picture *The Melton Hunt*, catalogue no. 58, includes a portrait of him), where his reputation for wild "Irish" behaviour was notorious. He is said to have "put aniseed on the hoofs of a parson's horse, and hunted the terrified divine with bloodhounds. On another occasion he put a donkey into the bed of a stranger at an inn. He took a hunting-box in the shires, and amused himself with shooting out the eyes of the family portraits with a pistol. He smashed a very valuable French clock on the staircase at Crockford's with a blow of his fist, and solemnly proposed to

one of the first railway companies in Ireland to start two engines in opposite directions on the same line in order that he might witness the smash, for which he proposed to pay."[11]

At home in Ireland, Lord Waterford hunted with the Tipperary Hunt, of which he was Master from 1840 to 1843. In F. C. Turner's scenes, dated 1842, he is depicted on a dapple-grey hunter in a central or leading role in each scene; but these pictures, engraved with the facetious title *The Noble Tips*, are not so much portraits from life as semi-satirical sketches, inspired by legends about "the wild Lord Waterford" and the Irish in general. In 1843 rioters tried to poison the Tipperary hounds and burnt down the Hunt stables. The Marquis of Waterford retreated to his own country and was Master of the Waterford Hounds from 1844 to his death in 1859.

Marriage, in 1842, was said to have made Lord Waterford "much more gentle and amiable," and by the time of his death (in the hunting-field) he was described, in the *Annual Register* of 1859, as "one of the best landlords and most improving cultivators in Ireland, and had become universally respected and popular." His widow, Louisa, Marchioness of Waterford, achieved quiet fame as a watercolourist and benefactress to her estates. Three of her portraits of Lord Waterford were reproduced, with a sympathetic account of him, in Augustus Hare's *Story of Two Noble Lives*.[12]

COLLECTIONS: Commissioned by J. W. Moore(?), Printseller and Publisher, London; Robert de Grey Vyner; J. Barry Donahue Fine Arts; acquired 1981.
ENGRAVING: By Hunt and Mackrell as *Moore's Tally-Ho! to the Sports: The Noble Tips*: (1) *Tipperary Boys* . . . ; (2) *Tipperary Melody* . . . ; (3) *Tipperary Glory* . . . ; (4) *Tipperary Killing, No Murder*, published by J. W. Moore, London, first issued 1842 (reprinted 1852–53).

[11] Ralph Nevill, *Sporting Days and Sporting Ways* (London: Duckworth & Co., 1910), pp. 7–8.
[12] Augustus J. C. Hare, *Two Noble Lives*, vol. 1 (1893), facing pp. 252 and 274; vol. 3, frontispiece.

CATALOGUE ENTRY 36

CATALOGUE ENTRY 37

CATALOGUE ENTRY 38

CATALOGUE ENTRY 39

Sporting artist and engraver whose vast output of drawings and prints is well represented in Paul Mellon's collection in the Virginia Museum of Fine Arts. Born in London, son of Samuel Alken, ornamental designer and engraver; learned engraving techniques; and trained as a miniature painter. Painted (more often in watercolour than oils) and engraved innumerable hunting, shooting, fishing, racing, and steeplechasing scenes, and subjects best summarized in one of Alken's own titles as Humorous Miscellanies.

40-41 *Fishing on the River Avon, Near Fording-bridge, Hampshire*, a pair, 1842
Trout Fishing at Harper Mill
Fishing for Pike

Oil on panel, each 17 x 24.25 (6³/₄ x 9¹/₂)

Inscribed on a rock, lower left, no. 40; on a branch, lower center, no. 41: *H. Alken / 1842*

Acc. Nos. 85.485.1/2

In catalogue no. 40 an angler holding a landing-net in his left hand wades a stream by an undershot mill and plays a fish. In catalogue no. 41 an angler has hooked a pike, and another fish lies on the riverbank beside a live-bait tin and a basket.

REFERENCES: Egerton, *Mellon Collection*, pp. 253–54, no. 276.
COLLECTIONS: Seymour Dalziell; Edward Speelman Ltd.; acquired 1963.

CATALOGUE ENTRY 40

CATALOGUE ENTRY 41

Painter of horses and dogs, hunting and coaching scenes. Born in Beccles,
Suffolk, son of Daniel Cooper, drawing master at Bury St. Edmunds School;
designated "of Beccles" to distinguish him from many other artists of the
same name. Worked at Newmarket, Norwich, and Cambridge, in oils and
watercolour.

42 *Waiting at the Meet*, 1832

Oil on canvas, 101.5 x 127 (40 x 50)

Inscribed, lower left: E^n Cooper Pinx^t / 1832

Acc. No. 85.486

Three riders—perhaps the Master, on the grey, with two hunt servants
in green livery—wait as members of the hunt ride in. In the foreground,
nine couple of hounds are decorously disposed on the sloping ground so
that each may be individually portrayed. Two hounds are coupled, no
doubt so that an experienced hound can educate the younger one in the
hunting-field, and the huntsman, dismounted from his dapple-grey on
the left, carries a spare coupling collar on his saddle.

REFERENCES: Egerton, *Mellon Collection*, p. 256, no. 282.
COLLECTIONS: The Viscount Curzon of Penn; Arthur Ackermann & Son Ltd.;
acquired 1961.
EXHIBITIONS: Arthur Ackermann & Son Ltd., *Annual Exhibition of XVIIIth & XIXth*
Century Sporting Paintings, 1961 (no. 7, illus. frontispiece).

CATALOGUE ENTRY 42

Sporting and animal painter; born in London, the son of a tobacconist. Largely self-taught as an artist, though given some tuition and much encouragement from Ben Marshall. Prolific exhibitor 1812–69, particularly at the Royal Academy; elected Royal Academician 1820. His subjects include hunters, racehorses, draught horses, shooting, deer-stalking, and animals newly imported into menageries; he also derived animal subjects from history and literature.

43 *The Wapiti or North American Deer*, 1818

Oil on panel, 27.5 x 36 (10⅞ x 14⅛)

Inscribed, lower right: *AC* [in monogram] / *1818*

Acc. No. 85.487

Cooper sketched the deer from the life in the King's Mews, near Charing Cross. Captured by a German naturalist in the Upper Missouri country, the deer had already been exhibited as curiosities in Baltimore, Philadelphia, and New York before being brought to London. The following description accompanied the engraving after Cooper's picture:

> The colour of these animals is, in the winter, on the body of a peculiar dunnish hue; the neck and legs are a dark brown; the rump is a pale yellowish white, the colour extending about six or seven inches from the tail on all sides, and very distinct from the general colour of the body. A black semi-circular line of unequal width (from a quarter of an inch to two inches) separates the white of the rump from the dun of the body. Their summer coat is thin, and the colour a reddish grey.
>
> The head resembles that of the common American deer (Cervus Virginianus) and of the horse, much more than that of the Elk or Moose, and is pointed and handsome. The legs are admirably formed for strength and activity, resembling those of the race horse, particularly the hinder. . . . The Wapiti has an oblique slit or opening under the inner angle of each eye, nearly an inch long externally, which appears to be an auxiliary nostril, and secretes a brown granulated substance. He has no voice, like the horse or the ox, and this organ seems to be given him as a compensation; for with it he makes a noise, which he can vary at pleasure, and which is like the loud and piercing whistle that boys give by putting their fingers in their mouth. . . .[13]

REFERENCES: Egerton, *Mellon Collection*, p. 261, no. 288.
COLLECTIONS: Painted for the Earl of Upper Ossory; Sabin Galleries; acquired 1971.
EXHIBITIONS: Royal Academy, 1818 (no. 23).
ENGRAVING: Before completion in 1818(?), or perhaps from a version, in the London art market 1983, by John Scott, published in *The Sporting Magazine* (November 1817): facing p. 49.

[13] *The Sporting Magazine* (November 1817): 50.

CATALOGUE ENTRY 43

SAMUEL JOHN EGBERT JONES (active 1820–1845)

Sporting, coaching, and landscape painter. His coaching, hunting, and
shooting scenes are usually set in well-observed landscapes. Nothing is known
of his life, and his work is chiefly known through engravings.

44 = 47 *Shooting*, a set of four, engraved 1845
Partridge Shooting, oil on panel
Pheasant Shooting, oil on panel
Woodcock Shooting, oil on canvas
Duck Shooting, oil on canvas

Average size, 35.5 x 45.75 (14 x 18)
Acc. Nos. 85.488.1/4

REFERENCES: Egerton, *Mellon Collection*, p. 266, no. 291.
COLLECTIONS: Ellis & Smith; Colonel John S. Alston; sold Christie's April 25, 1969
(nos. 98–99, illus.); bought by Arthur Ackermann & Son Ltd.; acquired 1969.
EXHIBITIONS: Arthur Ackermann & Son Ltd., *Annual Exhibition of Sporting Paintings*,
1969 (no. 22, illus.).
ENGRAVING: By H. Pyall, in aquatint, published by Hollyer, 1845.

CATALOGUE ENTRY 44

CATALOGUE ENTRY 45

CATALOGUE ENTRY 46

CATALOGUE ENTRY 47

Sporting and coaching painter and engraver. Born in Islington, London, son of Robert Pollard, engraver. At the age of fifteen, copied horses by Ben Marshall, and aspired to be a painter; meanwhile worked until his late twenties as draughtsman and engraver in his father's firm, his designs increasingly sought by other print publishers. Launched as a painter by the exhibition of a popular coaching picture at the Royal Academy, 1821. About 350 of his pictures were engraved, over half by himself. Best known for his coaching pictures; also painted many racing, hunting, and steeplechasing scenes. His paintings are almost always meticulously detailed. His drawing and engraving styles are well represented in drawings and prints included in the Mellon Collection in the Virginia Museum of Fine Arts.

48–49 *Doncaster Races, 1830,* a pair
Horses Starting for the St. Leger, 1831
Passing the Judges' Stand

Oil on canvas, 37 x 65 (14½ x 25½)

Inscribed on door panel of smaller coach, lower right of center, no. 48: *J. Pollard / 1831*

Acc. Nos. 85.489.1/2

By 1831 Pollard was very familiar with Doncaster Racecourse, where the classic St. Leger race was annually run. As early as 1823, Robert Pollard had reported to his friend Thomas Bewick, "My sons have been to Doncaster Races to take Views of the Stand & Portraits of Winning Horses to make Prints of our own Publishing."[14]

In catalogue no. 48 Pollard shows the field of twenty-eight horses waiting for the starter's signal, which he is about to give by the ancient but erratic method of lowering his arm and shouting "Go!" at the top of his voice. Spectators line the rails, crowd the stands, and perch on top of carriages. The passage of two stage-coaches through Doncaster has been carefully timed so that passengers can see the race; the smaller coach bears Pollard's name, the larger one is lettered *London—Leeds* and *Newark—Doncaster.*

Catalogue no. 49 shows the finish of the 1830 St. Leger, with Birmingham beating Priam by half a length, Emancipation a length behind them, Pedestrian fourth, and Brunswicker fifth, to the cheers of a huge crowd.

REFERENCES: N.C. Selway, *James Pollard 1792–1867* (Leigh-on-Sea, England: F. Lewis, 1965), no. 158, illus.; N. C. Selway, *The Golden Age of Coaching and Sport* (Leigh-on-Sea, England: F. Lewis, 1972), no. 186; Egerton, *Mellon Collection*, p. 273, no. 297.
COLLECTIONS: R. Younger; Arthur Ackermann & Son Ltd.; acquired 1965.
EXHIBITIONS: Catalogue no. 48, Arts Council of Great Britain, *British Sporting Painting 1650–1850,* 1974–75 (no. 169, illus. p. 101); Yale Center for British Art, *The Pursuit of Happiness, A View of Life in Georgian England,* 1977 (no. 153, illus.).
ENGRAVING: By Smart and Hunt, in aquatint, published by S. & J. Fuller (catalogue no. 48, June 1, 1832; catalogue no. 49, October 25, 1833).

[14] N. C. Selway, *James Pollard 1792–1867* (Leigh-on-Sea, England: F. Lewis, 1965).

CATALOGUE ENTRY 48

CATALOGUE ENTRY 49

50-53 *The Hertfordshire Hunt*, a set of four, 1839
Fox-Hunters' Meeting
Breaking Cover
A Fox Chase
The Death

Oil on canvas, each 40.75 x 56.25 (16 x 22⅛)

Inscribed, lower center, nos. 51, 52, 53: *J. Pollard 1839*

Acc. Nos. 85.490.1/4

The Hertfordshire Hunt was founded in 1822. Its country stretched from the Middlesex border in the south to include a part of Bedfordshire in the north, taking in most of the country west of the Puckeridge Hunt. The Master of the Hertfordshire Hunt in 1839 (the date of Pollard's paintings) was Frederick Peter Delmé Radcliffe; in the same year, he published a book which became a hunting classic, *The Noble Science, or a Few General Hints for the use of the Rising Generation, especially those of the Hertfordshire Hunt Club*, illustrated by his brother, the Reverend C. D. Radcliffe. F. P. Delmé Radcliffe, MFH (Master of Foxhounds), also wrote hunting ballads, and he was probably the author of the verses which appear on the engravings of *The Hertfordshire Hunt*.

REFERENCES: N. C. Selway, *The Golden Age of Coaching and Sport*, nos. 292–95, illus.; Egerton, *Mellon Collection*, p. 277, no. 302.
COLLECTIONS: Anonymous sale, Sotheby's March 18, 1970 (no. 117; catalogue nos. 50 and 52 illus.); bought by Arthur Ackermann & Son Ltd.; acquired 1970.
EXHIBITIONS: Arthur Ackermann & Son Ltd., *An Exhibition of Sporting Paintings*, 1970 (no. 16, illus.); Yale Center for British Art, *The Pursuit of Happiness, A View of Life in Georgian England*, 1977(no. 168, illus.).
ENGRAVING: By Charles Hunt, in aquatint, with titles as above followed by verses, published by T. Helme, 1840.

CATALOGUE ENTRY 50

CATALOGUE ENTRY 51

CATALOGUE ENTRY 52

CATALOGUE ENTRY 53

JOHN FREDERICK HERRING (1795–1865)

Sporting and animal painter. Son of a London fringe-maker; initially a self-taught artist, painting inn signs and coach panels while working as a night coachman in York and Doncaster. Launched by a commission to paint the winner of the St. Leger, 1815, the first of a long series of portraits of winners of classic races. Moved to London ca. 1830, and studied under Abraham Cooper. His later career was prosperous, and his patrons included Queen Victoria; his choice of subject-matter became more varied and more rural. Much of his work was engraved. His sons were John Frederick, Jr., who imitated his work; Charles, who assisted his father but died aged twenty-eight; and Benjamin, a sporting painter.

54 - 55   *Hunting Scenes*, a pair, ca. 1840
A Hunting Morn
Streaming Off

Oil on canvas; no. 54, 76.5 x 127.6 (30^{1}/$_{8}$ x 50^{1}/$_{4}$); no. 55, 77.2 x 128 (30^{3}/$_{8}$ x 50^{3}/$_{8}$)

Inscribed, lower left, no. 54; lower right, no. 55: *J F Herring*

Acc. Nos. 85.491.1/2

COLLECTIONS: Nancy B. Martin, Glyndon, Maryland; acquired 1977.

CATALOGUE ENTRY 54

CATALOGUE ENTRY 55

56 *Thomas Dawson and His Family*, 1842

Oil on canvas, 48 x 63.5 (19 x 25)

Inscribed, lower left: *Dawson of Middleham / 1842*

Acc. No. 85.492

Thomas Dawson was one of the most famous British racehorse trainers of his day. The eldest of the seventeen children of George Dawson, trainer to the twelfth Earl of Eglinton, he was born at Gullane, Haddington, Scotland, on February 7, 1809. In 1830 he left Scotland to establish his own training stables at Middleham, Yorkshire, where over the next fifty years he trained many Classic winners and acquired a high reputation, particularly as a trainer for long-distance races. He died at Middleham February 18, 1880.

Herring portrayed Dawson at the age of thirty-three, posing with his wife and children on a sunny day in spring 1842 outside his house at Tupgill, Middleham, Yorkshire. Dawson's small daughter is in his arms; his younger son Thomas Sutherland Dawson is perched on the wall beside him. Mrs. Dawson stands in the center of the group, with a sprig of apple blossom in her hand; on her left, George Sutherland Dawson, aged about five, rides a piebald pony, with the greyhound bitch, Grace Darling, beside him. Both the boys wear Glengarry bonnets, an echo of the family's Scottish origins.

REFERENCES: Egerton, *Mellon Collection*, pp. 305–6, no. 330, pl. 107.
COLLECTIONS: Painted for Thomas Dawson; by descent to Thomas Sutherland Dawson; anonymous sale Sotheby's March 12, 1969 (no. 173); bought by Thomas Agnew & Sons Ltd.; acquired 1969.

Painter of portraits, sporting, coaching, and military subjects. Pringle's life is obscure, but he appears to have been a professional painter in Birmingham, where he exhibited 1834–43; he is listed in Birmingham directories for 1841–45.

57 A Sportsman Talking to His Beater After Coursing, ca. 1830–40

Oil on canvas, 122 x 183 (48 x 72)
Acc. No. 85.493

A stout gentleman, clearly portrayed from life, stands talking to a beater who holds a dead hare in his right hand and a tall sapling wand in the other; another dead hare is slung over the saddle of the master's horse, while two greyhounds, four spaniels, and a terrier wait obediently. The composition is a little stiff and the figures and animals rather tightly drawn. The former attribution to Abraham Cooper is difficult to accept; the reattribution to Pringle was suggested by Alfred Gates of Arthur Ackermann & Son on the basis of the similarity of the figures and animals to those in signed works by Pringle.

REFERENCES: Egerton, *Mellon Collection*, pp. 325–26, no. 358, pl. 113.
COLLECTIONS: Oscar & Peter Johnson; acquired 1966 (as *A Sporting Conversation Piece* by Abraham Cooper).
EXHIBITIONS: Oscar & Peter Johnson, Lowndes Lodge Gallery, *Ward, Morland and their Circle*, 1966 (no. 32, as *A Sporting Conversation Piece* by Abraham Cooper).

CATALOGUE ENTRY 57

SIR FRANCIS GRANT, President of the Royal Academy (1803–1878)

Sporting and portrait painter. Born Edinburgh, son of a Perthsire laird; educated at Harrow. Began hunting at Melton Mowbray ca. 1820, set up his own hunting establishment by 1827 and maintained it until his death at Melton fifty years later. By the age of twenty-six, Grant had squandered his patrimony; having taken some lessons from John Ferneley, he decided to paint for a living and rapidly became a fashionable portrait painter. He enjoyed the patronage of Queen Victoria and painted approximately 800 portraits between 1831 and his death. Elected President of the Royal Academy in 1866.

58 The Melton Hunt Going to Draw the Ram's Head Cover, exhibited 1839

Oil on canvas, 91.5 x 152.5 (35¹⁵/₁₆ x 60)

Acc. No. 85.494

The exhibition of this picture at the Royal Academy in 1839 and its purchase from the artist by the first Duke of Wellington helped to make Francis Grant's name as a fashionable portrait painter. Grant exhibited it with the title *The Melton Hunt . . .*, by which he meant a hunt in the Leicestershire countryside around Melton Mowbray, center of some of the best fox-hunting in England. What he portrays is in fact a meet of the Quorn Hunt, attended by some of the most notable hunting men of the day from all over the kingdom; thirty-six portraits are identified by name both in the Royal Academy catalogue of 1839 and in a key plate to the engraving published the following year.

Correspondence in the present Duke of Wellington's possession records that the first Duke of Wellington was prompted to purchase the picture, for 500 guineas, by the Countess of Wilton. She is depicted in the center of the group, driving herself and her young son Lord Grey de Wilton in a phaeton drawn by a spirited pair of cream ponies. To the left of the phaeton, the pack is led off by Jennings and Tom Balls, first and second whippers-in (seen from behind), with Mr. Treadwell, the huntsman, keeping an eye on the hounds; in the foreground is Master Thomas Baird on a Shetland pony.

Just in front of the phaeton is the Master of the Quorn, Lord Suffield, raising his hand as a warning to the field not to press too hard on the pack as they move off; his brother-in-law, Lord Gardner, rides beside him. Beside the phaeton ride Lord Macdonald, the Earl of Darlington, and the Honourable Mrs. Villiers. Behind the phaeton, Lord Wilton, in a grey overcoat, leads a group which includes Walter Little Gilmour, laird of Liberton and Craigmillar, the Honourable Augustus Villiers, John White, Esq., Prince Rudolph Lichtenstein, Sir David Baird, the Earl of Rosslyn and Count Batthyany, with William Coke, Esq., the only rider in the group wearing trousers rather than breeches. The upper group of riders includes the Marquis of Waterford, putting his grey horse at a gate (he is depicted again in F. C. Turner's Tipperary hunting scenes, catalogue nos. 36–39), and his fellow Irishman, the Earl of Howth, with hat in hand.

The *Art-Union* of 1839 pronounced this picture to be "an epic of its class. None of what are usually termed 'sporting pictures,' of which the last century has been so fertile, are for a moment to be compared with it."

REFERENCES: *The Art-Union, A Monthly Journal of the Fine Arts* 1 (1839): 70–71; H. Clifford Smith, "Sir Francis Grant's Quorn Masterpiece," *Country Life* 3 (January 18, 1952): 152–53.

COLLECTIONS: Purchased from the artist by the first Duke of Wellington for 500 guineas; by descent to the eighth Duke of Wellington; sold Christie's June 22, 1979 (no. 79, illus.); bought by Arthur Ackermann & Son Ltd.; acquired 1979.

EXHIBITIONS: Royal Academy, 1839 (no. 545); Victoria and Albert Museum, *National Portrait Exhibition*, 1868 (no. 474); *Jubilee Exhibition*, Manchester, 1887 (no. 785); Royal Academy, *The First Hundred Years of the Royal Academy 1769–1868*, 1951 (no. 148); Manchester City Art Gallery, *Heaton Hall Bicentenary Exhibition*, 1972 (no. 114).

ENGRAVING: By W. Humphreys, in mixed method, as *The Meet at Melton*, published by Graves and Warmisley October 1, 1840, with an engraved key plate (re-issued November 1, 1841).

CATALOGUE ENTRY 58

SELECT BIBLIOGRAPHY

The following list provides suggestions for further reading.

Abbey, J. R. *Life in England 1770–1860*. London: Privately printed at the Curwen Press, 1953.

Boalch, D. H. *Prints and Paintings of British Farm Livestock 1780–1910: A Record of The Rothamsted Collection*. Harpenden: 1958.

Bovill, E. W. *The England of Nimrod and Surtees 1815–1854*. London: Oxford University Press, 1959.

Carr, Raymond. *English Fox Hunting*. London: Weidenfeld and Nicolson, 1976.

Egerton, Judy. *The Paul Mellon Collection, British Sporting and Animal Paintings 1655–1867*. London: The Tate Gallery for the Yale Center for British Art, 1978.

Egerton, Judy, and Dudley Snelgrove. *The Paul Mellon Collection, British Sporting and Animal Drawings c. 1500–1850*. London: The Tate Gallery for the Yale Center for British Art, 1978.

Gilbey, Sir Walter. *Animal Painters of England from the Year 1650*. 3 vols. London: Vinton and Company, 1900–11.

——. *George Morland*. London: A. and C. Black, 1907.

Graves, Algernon. *The Royal Academy of Arts; A Complete Dictionary of Contributors and Their Work from Its Foundation in 1769 to 1904*. 8 vols. 1905–06. Reprint (8 vols. in 4). New York: B. Franklin, 1972.

——. *The Society of Artists of Great Britain 1760–1791; The Free Society of Artists 1761–1783: A Complete Dictionary of Contributors*. London: G. Bell and Sons, 1907.

Grundy, C. Reginald. *James Ward R. A.* London: Otto Ltd., 1909.

Hammelmann, Hanns A. *Book Illustrators in Eighteenth Century England*. Edited and completed by T. S. R. Boase. New Haven: Yale University Press, 1975.

Hutchison, Sidney C. *The History of the Royal Academy 1768–1968*. London: Chapmann and Hall, 1968.

Irwin, David, and Francina Irwin. *Scottish Painters at Home and Abroad 1700–1900*. London: Faber, 1975.

Longrigg, Roger. *The English Squire and his Sport*. New York: St. Martin's Press, 1977.

——. *The History of Foxhunting*. London: MacMillan, 1975.

——. *The History of Horse Racing*. London: MacMillan, 1972.

Millar, Oliver. *British Sporting Painting 1650–1850*. London: Arts Council of Great Britain, 1974–75.

Mortimer, Roger. *The Jockey Club*. London: Cassell and Company, 1958.

Noakes, Aubrey. *Ben Marshall, 1768–1835*. Leigh-on-Sea, England: F. Lewis, 1978.

——. *The World of Henry Alken*. London: Witherby, 1952.

Paget, Guy. *Sporting Pictures of England*. London: Collins, 1945.

Pavière, Sydney H. *A Dictionary of British Sporting Painters*. 1965. Reprint. Leigh-on-Sea, England: F. Lewis, 1980.

Selway, N. C. *The Golden Age of Coaching and Sport*. Leigh-on-Sea, England: F. Lewis, 1972.

——. *James Pollard 1792–1867*. Leigh-on-Sea, England: F. Lewis, 1965.

Siltzer, Frank. *Newmarket*. London: Cassell and Company, 1923.

Smith, H. Clifford. "Sir Francis Grant's Quorn Masterpiece," *Country Life* 3 (January 18, 1952): 152–53.

Snelgrove, Dudley. *The Paul Mellon Collection, British Sporting and Animal Prints 1658–1874.* London: The Tate Gallery for the Yale Center for British Art, 1981.

Sparrow, Walter Shaw. *A Book of Sporting Painters.* London: John Lane, 1931.

——. *British Sporting Artists.* London: John Lane, 1922. Reprint, 1965.

Taylor, Basil. *Animal Painting in England from Barlow to Landseer.* Harmondsworth: Penguin Books, 1955.

——. *Painting in England 1700–1850: Collection of Mr. and Mrs. Paul Mellon.* Exhibition catalogue. 2 vols. Richmond: Virginia Museum of Fine Arts, 1963.

——. *Sport and the Horse.* Exhibition catalogue. Richmond: Virginia Museum of Fine Arts, 1960.

Van Devanter, Willis. "A Checklist of Books Illustrated by Henry Alken." In *Homage to a Bookman.* Berlin: Mann, 1967.

Walker, Stella A. *Sporting Art: England 1700–1900.* New York: Clarkson N. Potter, 1972.

Waterhouse, Ellis. *Paintings in Britain: 1530–1790.* 2nd ed. Baltimore: Penguin Books, 1962.

Whitley, William T. *Artists and their Friends in England 1700–1799.* 2 vols. London: The Medici Society, 1928.

Wood, J. C. *A Dictionary of British Animal Painters.* Leigh-on-Sea, England: F. Lewis, 1973.

INDEX OF ARTISTS

OTHER CATALOGUES OF THE COLLECTIONS OF
THE VIRGINIA MUSEUM OF FINE ARTS

Fabergé: A Catalog of the Lillian Thomas Pratt Collection of Russian Imperial Jewels (1960; rev. 1976)

European Art in the Virginia Museum (1966)

Ancient Art in the Virginia Museum (1973)

Treasures in the Virginia Museum (1974)

The Sydney and Frances Lewis Contemporary Art Fund Collection (1980)

Eighteenth-Century Meissen Porcelain from the Margaret M. and Arthur J. Mourot Collection in the Virginia Museum (1983)

Oriental Rugs: The Collection of Dr. and Mrs. Robert A. Fisher in the Virginia Museum of Fine Arts (1984)

French Paintings: The Collection of Mr. and Mrs. Paul Mellon in the Virginia Museum of Fine Arts (1985)

Late 19th and Early 20th Century Decorative Arts: The Sydney and Frances Lewis Collection in the Virginia Museum of Fine Arts (1985)

Late 20th Century Art: Selections from the Sydney and Frances Lewis Collection in the Virginia Museum of Fine Arts (1985)

VIRGINIA MUSEUM OF FINE ARTS STAFF

British Sporting Paintings Catalogue Project

Paul N. Perrot, Director; Stephen G. Brown, Deputy Director; David B. Bradley, Director/Development Office; Richard B. Woodward, Manager/Office of Art Services; Patricia Bayer, Assistant Manager/Office of Art Services; Mary Moore Jacoby, Photographic Services Coordinator; Lisa Hummel, Registrar; Betty A. Stacy, Librarian

Curatorial: Pinkney L. Near, Chief Curator; Elizabeth McGarry, Collections Division Secretary

Publications: George Cruger, Manager/Publications Office; Anne B. Barriault, Project Editor and Editor/Publications Office; Monica M. Hamm, Senior Editor; Donald Spanel, Editor; Raymond Geary, Chief Graphic Designer; Will Flynn, Graphic Designer; Sarah Lavicka, Graphic Designer; Carolyn Maxey, Publications Office Secretary; Diana Vincelli, Clerical Assistant

The Virginia Museum of Fine Arts wishes to acknowledge Beverly Carter, Administrative Assistant, Paul Mellon Collection, for her assistance and cooperation, and the National Gallery of Art, Washington, D.C., for photographs of catalogue entry nos. 5, 8, and 27 by José Naranjo.

This book was composed in Linoterm Baskerville and printed
on acid-free Warren's Lustro Offset Enamel Dull paper by
Meriden-Stinehour Press, of Meriden, Connecticut, and Lunenburg, Vermont.